Motherhood

NOTES

Canadian representatives: General Publishing Co., Ltd.,
30 Lesmill Road, Don Mills, Ontario M3B 2T6.

ISBN 1–56138–483–6

Cover design by Toby Schmidt
Interior design by Christian Benton
Cover and interior illustrations by Valerie Coursen
Typography by Deborah Lugar
Printed in the United States

This book may be ordered by mail from the publisher.
Please add $1.00 for postage and handling.
But try your bookstore first!

Running Press Book Publishers
125 South Twenty-second Street
Philadelphia, Pennsylvania 19103–4399

Motherhood

NOTES

RUNNING PRESS
PHILADELPHIA · LONDON

*I*n the beginning there was my mother. A shape. A shape and a force, standing in the light. You could see her energy, it was visible in the air. Against any background she stood out. . . .

MARILYN KRYSL
20TH-CENTURY AMERICAN WRITER

Your mother loves you like the deuce while you are coming. Wrapped up there under her heart is perhaps the cosiest time in existence. Then she and you are one, companions.

Emily Carr (1871–1945)
Canadian artist

Life is the first gift,

love is the second,

and understanding

the third.

Marge Piercy, b. 1934
American writer

His first breath was pressed into him. I should have thought of something poetic to say. . . . This was, after all, the only personal miracle I had ever known. I just whispered, "Thanks," and the wonderful thing is I was thanking myself.

GAIL PARENT, B. 1940
AMERICAN WRITER

The midwife asked me if I would like to see the child. "Please," I said gratefully. . . . She put her in my arms and I sat there looking at her, and her great wide blue eyes looked at me with seeming recognition, and what I felt it is pointless to try to describe.

Margaret Drabble, b. 1939
British writer

. . . the child and her feeling for it were somehow absolute, truer and more binding than any other experience life had to offer: she felt she lived at the blind true core of life.

Marilyn French, b. 1929
American writer

$\mathcal{I}$ remember leaving the hospital . . . thinking, "Wait, are they going to let me just walk off with him? I don't know beans about babies!"

ANNE TYLER, B. 1941
AMERICAN WRITER

. . . it is still the biggest gamble in the world. It is the glorious life force. It's huge and scary—it's an act of infinite optimism.

Gilda Radner (1946–1989)
American actress and writer

I'd forgotten how sensual life
becomes with a new baby.
Where do women get the idea
motherhood makes them less
desirable to men?

Elizabeth Forsythe Hailey, b. 1938
American writer

Children grow up, not in a smooth
ascending curve, but jaggedly, their
needs inconstant as weather.

ADRIENNE RICH, B. 1929
AMERICAN WRITER

. . . how deep a child's love goes. It is more thorough than adult love.

I loved not only my parents: I loved their love.

Josephine Humphreys, b. 1945
American writer

[My role is to release my children] full force on the world, loving themselves, loving what's different about themselves, embracing what's different about other people, and up for some kind of adventure.

Susan Sarandon, b. 1947
American actress

A mother is a mother still,
The holiest thing alive.

SAMUEL TAYLOR COLERIDGE (1772–1834)
ENGLISH POET

A child's kiss

Set on thy sighing lips

shall make thee glad . . .

Thou shalt be served

thyself by every sense

Of service which

thou renderest.

Elizabeth Barrett Browning (1806–1861)
English poet

"*You* are the caretaker of the generations, you are the birth giver," the sun told the woman. "You will be the carrier of this universe."

Brule Sioux sun creation myth

If a child is to keep alive his inborn sense of wonder without any such gift from the fairies, he needs the companionship of at least one adult who can share it. . . .

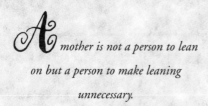

A mother is not a person to lean on but a person to make leaning unnecessary.

Dorothy Canfield Fisher (1879–1958)
American writer

... there's a lot more to being a
woman than being a mother,
but there's a hell of a lot more
to being a mother than most
people suspect.

Roseanne Arnold, b. 1952
American comedian and actress

She's had to learn motherhood on a wing and a prayer in the last three years, and right now her main philosophy is that everything truly important is washable.

BARBARA KINGSOLVER, B. 1955
AMERICAN WRITER

*Ask your child
what he wants
for dinner
only if he's
buying.*

Fran Lebowitz, b. 1951
American writer

The real menace in dealing with a five-year-old is that in no time at all you begin to sound like a five-year-old.

Jean Kerr, b. 1923
American playwright

My mother had a great deal of trouble
with me, but I think she enjoyed it.

MARK TWAIN (1835–1910)
AMERICAN WRITER

In a child's lunch box,
a mother's thoughts.

Japanese proverb

*B*efore becoming a mother I had a hundred theories on how to bring up children. Now I have seven children and only one theory: love them, especially when they least deserve to be loved.

Kate Sanperi
20th-century American writer

We spend half our lives rebelling against our mothers and the next half against our daughters.

LOIS WYSE, B. 1926
AMERICAN WRITER

Children begin by loving their parents; as they grow older they judge them; sometimes they forgive them.

Oscar Wilde (1854–1900)
Irish writer

Motherhood is not a one-size-fits-all. . . . No Mother is all good or all bad, all laughing or all serious, all loving or all angry. Ambivalence runs through their veins. . . . It is not until you become a mother that your judgment slowly turns to compassion and understanding.

Erma Bombeck, b. 1927
American writer

*F*or every woman,
there are always three women:

1) girl-baby;

2) mother;

3) mother's mother.

D. W. WINNICOTT
20TH-CENTURY AMERICAN WRITER

*The best protection against death
is giving birth.*

African proverb

You can get divorced and live to tell about it. You can miss out on a promotion and try again next year. You cannot, however, fail at child-rearing and sleep at night.

Anita Shreve, b. 1946
American writer

Good parents raise children who are competent and confident enough to leave them. What a deal.

ELLEN GOODMAN, B. 1941
AMERICAN JOURNALIST

The best way to keep children at home is to make home a pleasant atmosphere—and to let the air out of the tires.

Dorothy Parker (1893–1967)
American writer

Whereas the service rendered the United States by the
American mother is the greatest source of the country's
strength and inspiration. . . . Whereas the American mother
is doing so much for the home, for moral spirits and religion,
hence so much for good government and humanity. . . .
Therefore, be it resolved that the second Sunday in May
will be celebrated as Mother's Day.

U.S. Congress, 1914

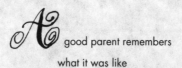

good parent remembers
what it was like
to be a child.

ANNA QUINDLEN, B. 1952
AMERICAN WRITER

When I stopped seeing myself with the eyes of a child, I saw the woman who helped me give birth to myself.

Nancy Friday, b. 1937
American writer

Love . . . had a strange way of multiplying. Doubling.
Trebling itself, so that, as each child arrived, there was
always more than enough to go around.

Rosamunde Pilcher, b. 1924
British writer

$\mathcal{G}$od could not be everywhere, so he made mothers.

PROVERB

You are the gate through which it came into the world, and you will be allowed to have charge of it for a period; after that it will leave you and blossom out into its own free life—and there it is, for you to watch, living its life in freedom.

Agatha Christie (1890–1976)
English writer

From out the mother

shines the child.

Muriel Rukeyser (1913–1980)
American poet